The s...

CW00841582

**M**ysti Rainbowfrost, a real fairy, has been assigned to keep an eye on cool teenager, Ella Devonshire. After a difficult start, the two have become friends. Mysti is fascinated by the human world and Ella rather likes the help a fairy friend can bring.

But it's not all been plain sailing, and it would be boring if it were. Ella's relationship with Ollie is lacking romantic magic and it looks like Thorn Oakwood, her fairy heart-throb, has spurned Mysti. And there's trouble brewing in fairyland in a battle that threatens to spill over into the human world.

Ella
xx

Thorn Oakwood

Ollie

Mysti x

It is the end of term; Mrs Battye is taking an English class, exploring the deeper meaning of Romeo and Juliet...

5

11

# Drow Elves

We've put this off long enough, so we'd probably better deal with these bad boys now. The Drow are also known as "The Lost Elves". This doesn't mean that they need a map - if they had one they'd probably slice it up into little bits...

Getting the picture now, aren't you? The Drow are permanently flacked off, as they don't get to run around and play happy fairies. They disgraced themselves in a war for supremacy with the elves thousands of years ago. Now they secretly plot revenge and will cause chaos wherever they can. Take this problem with the humans and the fairies for example: do you think they really care about what the humans are doing to the forest, or is it just a good excuse to kick the hell out of everyone? We're not going to answer this for you. All we'll say is this: The Drow hate puppies. And kittens. You see? All very male...

The Drow Elves' cave...

35

The Heath...

43

Hi, Ska... it's me... We were supposed to meet at the cinema... If you get this message will you call me back please?

The Heath…

A... A... Aitchoooooo! Er, what is that?

Help... I have to get out of here...

Mysti and Thorn set off...

50

51

# Frozen food factory...

55

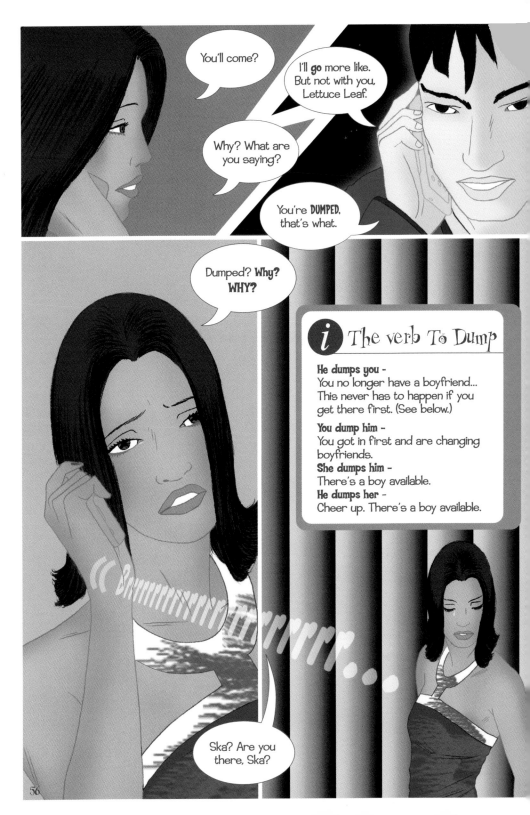

Sky at night…

Ella's bedroom, night…

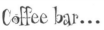

61

They have Gold Dust mu-mother...

Then this is serious. As ugly as they are in Drow form, so they will be handsome in human form. It is worse than I feared. As Drow, their power is limited to the Hidden World... but as humans it would be unthinkable... More MISCHIEF than we could imagine. We have to stop them.

## *i* Mischief/Miss Cheef

Rap artist. Not to be confused with Misteeq, Miss Dynamite, Missy Elliot, Miss D. Meanor Miss Fit and Miss Take. (Sorry, that last one was a mistake... No, not Miss Take... a mistake... Oh forget it. Read on.)

They're all jumping on the bandwagon but Miss Cheef was the original bad gal of pop. Why? You really want to know? OK. Don't say you weren't warned. Miss Cheef has bad words in her songs. Miss Cheef wears bad garms. Like ripped knickers. These are big knickers like you'd see on Gran's washing line... but ripped so they look cool. And she wears her bra back to front with a T-shirt over the top. (Try it, it's kinda weird. Especially from the back.)

As we have heard, the Goldress fears that under the Drow Elves' influence, all girls will look like Miss Cheef. Yes. Even you. So they have to be stopped.

 Aunt Saskia

Ella's mum's sister. Unmarried. A seriously cool aunty. She buys her clothes in Miss Sixty and drives a red convertible. Hers is the first present Ella opens on Christmas Day. She has taste. She's fun.

 Uncle George

No blood relation, thank God. He's a friend of granny's who insists on being called Uncle George. He must have over a hundred nieces and nephews, which is kinda weird if you think about it. He buys his clothes in Bumpkins & Son and drives a rusty red Lada. Ella wouldn't open a present from Uncle George if she were paid to. He sends boxes of chocolates he won in a raffle before they invented sell by dates. He has no taste. Ditto fun. Thankfully he has only come to drop Granny off.

 Granny

Cute little old lady and mother of Saskia and Ella's mum. She knits all her own clothes and drives a silver Zimmer frame. She has many faults, all of which are excused by the fact that she is very, very old. No, older than that...

That night, in Abby's room...

Suddenly...

Night, Ella.

Night.

Snore.

70

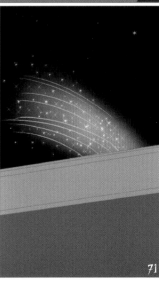

71

81

## Ella's room...

## Professor Dust is talking with some Sprites...

Mysti's bedroom...

Cor! Who's that?

He's from my drama club... I've fancied him for ages but he never spoke to me before.

He's pretty fit - go Rachael...

Thanks... you know... for inviting me and - Who's that?

Ska. He came to the vent, remember? Look, I'll catch up with you later, OK?

91

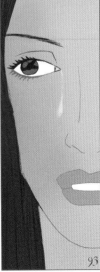

94

## ℹ Sheets

Large pieces of material neatly arranged on your bed daily by fairies until one day, without warning, your mother suddenly reveals, in a furious and dramatic way, that it has been her all along. And, while you are still getting over that shock, she reveals, more alarmingly still, that you are now old enough to do it yourself.

Hey, let's go... mess around between the SHEETS...

Er... excuse me... You can't go upstairs; my dad's left our Rottweiler up there and he doesn't like strangers.

Ella, there's something wrong with Lettie...

Go away splatface... Can't you see I'm busy.

Do I know you?

Don't think so...

105

## The Gnome Achilles' Heel

We told you how the gnomes would love to take over the world. Well, there's a problem. Unfortunately (especially for the gnomes), they are genetically compelled to try and fish at the first sign of any liquid - puddles, splash of water, goldfish bowl, you name it. Drives the poor little fellas mad, but they just have to try. In this case, half a skanky bottle of beer stops what would otherwise have been a terrifying attack of the gnomes... (sorry!) It's a tough life, living in the hidden world.

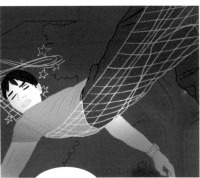

117

119

125

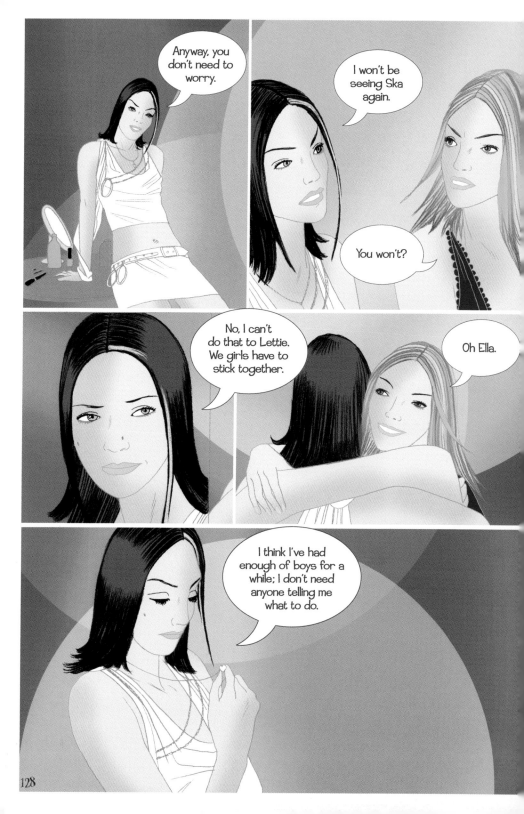